3 9082 02119092 4

THE STARS ARE SILVER REINDEER

For Catherine Louise Clayton

by NATALIA BELTING · *illustrated by* ESTA NESBITT

HOLT, RINEHART *and* WINSTON   *New York*   *Chicago*   *San Francisco*

THE STARS ARE SILVER REINDEER

Natalia Belting's interest in historical research which resulted
in THE SUN IS A GOLDEN EARRING, runner-up for the 1963 Caldecott
Award, CALENDAR MOON, an ALA Notable Book, and THE EARTH IS ON A
FISH'S BACK, has led her to legends of the constellations, which
provide the background for her poetic interpretations in THE
STARS ARE SILVER REINDEER. Besides writing children's books,
Miss Belting, a Ph.D., is assistant professor of history at
University of Illinois and enjoys gardening and excavating ancient
Indian artifacts from her property.

Before beginning her illustration of THE STARS ARE
SILVER REINDEER, Esta Nesbitt did extensive research on the
constellations and this artistic concern is reflected in the
unusual and distinctive technique she has used to interpret
Miss Belting's text—a technique particularly suited to the
subject matter of the book.
This same concern for finding the appropriate medium
of expression for every book she illustrates is apparent in
her distinguished work on JON THE UNLUCKY by Elizabeth Coats-
worth and THE EARTH IS ON A FISH'S BACK by Natalia Belting.
Mrs. Nesbitt and her family live in New York City.

1.
The stars are silver reindeer,
Or fishes swimming,
Water lilies,
Kangaroos.

They are fires the ghosts have lit,
A woman's silver necklace,
Holes in the canopy of heaven.

They are the dwelling place of gods,
Tents of rock crystal,
Shining paths of ice.

They are patterns the gods have set for men,
They are the fabric of men's dreams,
They are the handiwork of Yahweh.

The stars are silver reindeer.

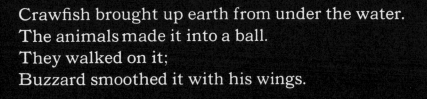

Crawfish brought up earth from under the water.
The animals made it into a ball.
They walked on it;
Buzzard smoothed it with his wings.

Panther walked in the sky for light,
But he gave too much light.

Spider walked in the sky,
But Spider's light was too dim.

The animals made Sun;
They set Moon in the night sky.

Chipmunk spoke: "Dark is still too dark."

The animals sent Spider to help Moon.
Then dark became just dark enough.

Spider is the ancestor of the stars.

YUCHI INDIANS,
SOUTHEASTERN UNITED STATES

2.

The star children dwelt in a deep cave,
Played at the foot of the Great Mountain,
And the earth was dark in the night.
The sky was naked,
Having no ornaments.

Then Kewa called them,
Kewa, brother of Tane, god of light.
They came at his voice,
Rolling up the side of the mountain,
Rolling, for they were round and had no legs.

They were put in baskets,
In the basket of the Sun,
In the basket of Moon, the Year Builder,
In the basket of Wide Space.

They were borne in Uruao, the canoe,
Piercer-of-the-clouds,
Borne to the sky, swiftly,
Carefully, so they were not jostled
Against each other and bruised.

They were borne to Tane
Who set them in the sky,
To make light for the earth,
To be ornaments for the sky.

POLYNESIA   The tail of Scorpio is the canoe, Uruao.

3.

The three flutes are in the flute house;
The sacred flutes are in the *jakui*
In the middle of the village.

The Sun gave the flutes to men,
Taught them the tunes to play,
Taught them the dances to dance

When the large cicada begins to sing,
And the rains commence
And the rivers rise;

When the fruit of the *piqui* tree ripens,
And the guardian of the tree must be honored;

When the rains end,
And the fields dry,
And the food grows scarce,

Men play the sacred flutes,
The great flutes,
And dance
As they were taught by the Sun,
Their ancestor.

INDIANS OF MATO GROSSO,
BRAZIL

Gemini is the flute
Castor and Pollux are the two holes
near the lower end of the flute.

4.
The Sing-Bonga beheld men
Scratching the earth with sticks,
With peacock tails,
With porcupine quills.

He went to the celestial blacksmith,
Took the plow he had used to plow the heavens
For a pattern.
Then the blacksmith blew on his fire with a bellows.
Made the charcoal burn red, burn hot,
Forged an iron plow for men
Like the plow of the Sing-Bonga

MUNDAS OF CHOTA-NAGUR,
CENTRAL INDIA

The Sword and Belt of Orion are the plow.
Capella and the Kids in Auriga are the
blacksmith, bellows, and fire.

5.

Si Jura carved a house post,
To honor Bali Utong, who brings prosperity,
Set up the post, with a pot of red leaves beside it;
Watched the messengers of the god,
The hawks, in flight; took omens from them,
Determined a time for a sea voyage
To find food
For the days when the rains ceased
And the earth dried in the furious heat.

His canoe brought him to a great tree,
Where it stood with its roots in the sky
And its limbs washing in the sea.

Si Jura climbed it to the sky.
Si Kera, the sky-dweller, made him welcome,
Set boiled rice,
Set paddy in a bowl before him,
Told him to eat the strange food.

Si Kera showed him the paddy stars overhead,
The seven rice stars shining,
The sign for the time of planting,
And gave him seed,
Instructions for building a storehouse.

Then Si Jura returned down a rope
To his own house, to his village,
Returned, brought paddy to men,
Brought food for men.

DYAKS OF SARAWAK

Pleiades, the rice stars,
are the bowl of boiled rice;
Pegasus is the storehouse.

6.

He who bound the dragons of Chaos,
Marduk, who cast down the dragons of darkness,
Made a canopy of skin
And stretched it for a sky.
He appointed the stations of the sun,
Set the path of it through the heavens,
Made the eastern gate for the sun to rise through,
The western gate for the setting sun.

He set the gods to manage the affairs of heaven and earth,
And they built a temple for Marduk,
The tower of Babel.
They built it on the edge of the primeval sea,
A stepped temple, a ziggurat of five levels,
According to the pattern they found among the stars.

Then they feasted,
Spread a feast before Marduk and were merry.
And Marduk was among them,
His scimitar on the table in their midst,
While the gods sang his praises in hymns,
Poured libations to honor him.

BABYLONIA

Aries and Cetus are the Tower of Babel.
Eridanus is the primeval sea.
Canis major is the scimitar.
Pisces is a fish near the temple.

7.
The bowlegged god, Bes,
The dwarf god
From the east,
Dwells among the stars.

Bes, in his leopard's skin,
Bes, with his lion's mane,
Bes, with a feather crown
And flowers in his hands,
Is at home among the stars,

Keeping evil spirits from the newborn sun,
Strangling serpents that would harm it.

Bes, the merry god,
Drinks through a straw,
Contorts his face,
And children laugh,
And are not afraid,
For Bes guards them.

EGYPT

Ophiuchus is Bes.
Serpens is the Serpent.

The river flows run through the sky land.
Giant blue lilies, pink water lilies.
Grow thick in it,
And fish swarm among the stems.

The camps of the star people are along the river.
The men stalk the kangaroos across the sky,
Hunt emus and wallabies and bandicoots with spears.
They fish with long lines,
Standing in their canoes.

The women gather seed pods from the lilies,
Lily stems to eat raw; they wait for the men
Where the fires burn to hot coals on the sands,
Where the smoke and the flames curl over the water.

ARNHEM LAND, AUSTRALIA

Milky Way:
Stars in it are lilies and some of the bigger fish.
Rifts are the canoes.
The general mistiness of some of its areas are
the smoke and flames from the fires.

Lynx:
The two largest stars are fires.
Other stars are childless old people
who hunt across the sky and cook on the fires.

Orion:
The belt is the three fishermen.
The sword is the line with the fish they have caught.
The smaller stars are children of the fishermen.

The Pleiades are the wives of fishermen,
in a canoe.

Scorpio is the crocodile,
opossum, and ibis.

9.
The spindles are still
And the spinning wheels quiet.
There is no flax spun
On the eve of Frigg's day.

Frigg, the beloved,
Wife to Odin,
First among the goddesses,
Takes up her spindle,
Sits before her wheel,
In Fensalir, the Sea Hall.

Frigg, who knows that which is to come,
Who tends the marriages of men,
And makes love grow between man and wife,
Frigg spins.
She only spins,
On the eve of her day,
On the eve of Friday.

SWEDEN

Orion:
The belt is the spindle and distaff.
The rest of the stars are
her spinning wheel.

10.

The men fashion the frames of their kayaks,
The women, together, sew on the skins,
Sew with ivory needles, or needles of rabbit teeth.

The men set off, some to hunt walrus,
And a seal hunter dips his double-blade oar
Into the freezing water,
Sends his kayak down the sky's icy river.

ALEUTIAN INDIANS

Milky Way is the river
Cygnus is the kayak, oar,
and seal hunter.

11.
The Sun drives copper-colored reindeer,
But the reindeer that stand in the Pebbly River at night,
The reindeer hitched to the sledge
On the riverbank are silver.
A white fox gnaws on some antlers,
And the elk pursued by the hunters,
The seal basking by the river,
And the polar bear are white.

The house of the Polar Star is rock-crystal ice.
A light burns on the roof of it.

And the children who live in the land of the sky
Coast on their sleds down icy hills
When Eagle has scraped the clouds off them.

CHUCKEE, NORTHEASTERN SIBERIA

Auriga is the Siberian sled with two reindeer pulling it.
Capella is the reindeer tied at the back of the sled.
Beta Auriga is the scarf of the driver.

Gemini:
Castor and Pollux are two elk running away from two hunters.
Other stars are the fox approaching the elk from one side.

Delphinus is the seal. The four main stars
are the body and flippers.

Corona Borealis is the paw of the polar bear.

Ursa Major is the six hunters with sling shots
and the fox gnawing antlers.

Cassiopeia is the five reindeer
wading in the Milky Way (Pebbly River).

Shooting stars are the children
sledding down hills.

12.
It is time for a Night Chant,
Time for dances and songs,
For prayers and sand paintings,
To bring healing to one who is sick.

The gourd rattles are made
With small stones inside,
And handles out of wood.
They are covered with designs punched out,
The figure of the North god,
The figure of the South god,
After the pattern of the stars overhead.

The dancers execute the steps,
The chants are sung
On the dance ground,
In the lodge,
To the accompaniment of rattles.

Then the god comes,
Comes in at the door of the lodge
Where the sick one is,
Eats the dish set out for him,
Says, "Your body is strong again,
"Your body is healed, it is holy."

NAVAHO INDIANS

The star patterns on the rattles
include Auriga, Ursa Major,
the Pleiades, Hyades, and Taurus.

13.

Gull taught men to use manioc for food,
And Dogfish planted the first field for them,
Dogfish, whom Gull called up from the river,
Gull, whom the Creator made,
By blowing smoke from his pipe
Upon a white gourd and some feathers.

They taught men to sow manioc,
To hoe and to harvest it,
And the women to prepare it for eating,
To cut it with shell knives,
Grate it with thorn graters,
Press it through bamboo sieves,
Boil it in red and black pots,
Dry the pulp upon great racks
Outside, back of their houses.

Gull and Dogfish taught men to use manioc for food.

INDIANS OF MATO GROSSO, BRAZIL

Orion is the large frame for drying manioc. Larger stars are the tops of posts.
Sirius is the end of the cross beam supporting the frame from the side.
Pleiades is the heap of grated manioc.
Aldebaran is the ball of pulp.

14.

Sibu, the god-who-builds,
Finished building the earth,
Finished sowing maize,
Finished making fish from the yucca,
Finished making deer from the large plantain,
And monkeys from alligator pears,
Finished making man by thinking about him.

Sibu gathered canes to build a house for himself,
Gathered palm leaves for the roof,
Sent men down under the earth to the east,
Five men to get a whisker from the great serpent,
To tie the palm leaves together.

Five men and five men more,
Five men, and again five men;
And the five men Sibu sent,
It took to roll up the whisker and lift it, and carry it to Sibu.

Sibu finished his house,
Tied the palm leaves together for the roof,
As man does, but not with vines.

The sky is the roof of Sibu's house,
The stars are the knots in the serpent's whisker.

TALAMANCAN INDIANS,
COSTA RICA

2.
The star children dwelt in a deep cave,

The tail of Scorpio is the canoe, Uruao.

3.
The three flutes are in the flute house;

Gemini is the flute
Castor and Pollux are the two holes
near the lower end of the flute.

4.
The Sing-Bonga beheld men

The Sword and Belt of Orion are the plow.
Capella and the Kids in Auriga are the
blacksmith, bellows, and fire.

5.
Si Jura carved a house post,

Pleiades, the rice stars,
are the bowl of boiled rice;
Pegasus is the storehouse.

[H]e who bound the dragons of Chaos,

[Ar]ies and Cetus are the Tower of Babel.
[Er]idanus is the primeval sea.
[Ca]nis major is the scimitar.
[Pi]sces is a fish near the temple.

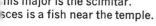
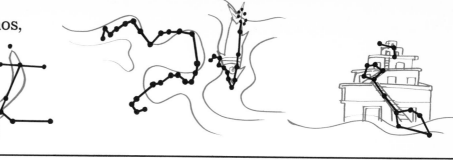

[T]he bowlegged god, Bes,

[Op]hiuchus is Bes.
[Se]rpens is the Serpent.

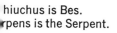

[T]he river flows full through the sky land.

[Mi]lky Way:
[Sta]rs in it are lilies and some of the bigger fish.
[Boa]ts are the canoes.
[Th]e general mistiness of some of its areas are
[th]e smoke and flames from the fires.

[Aja]x:
[Th]e two largest stars are fires.
[Oth]er stars are childless old people
[wh]o hunt across the sky and cook on the fires.

[Ori]on:
[Th]e belt is the three fishermen.
[Th]e sword is the line with the fish they have caught.
[Th]e smaller stars are children of the fishermen.

[Th]e Pleiades are the wives of fishermen,
[in a] canoe.

[Sco]rpio is the crocodile,
[opo]ssum, and ibis.

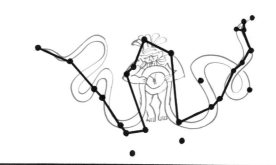

9.
The spindles are still

Orion:
The belt is the spindle and distaff.
The rest of the stars are
her spinning wheel.

10.
The men fashion the frames of their kayaks,

Milky Way is the river
Cygnus is the kayak, oar,
and seal hunter.

11.
The Sun drives copper-colored reindeer,

Auriga is the Siberian sled with two reindeer pulling it.
Capella is the reindeer tied at the back of the sled.
Beta Auriga is the scarf of the driver.

Gemini:
Castor and Pollux are two elk running away from two hunters.
Other stars are the fox approaching the elk from one side.

Delphinus is the seal. The four main stars
are the body and flippers.

Corona Borealis is the paw of the polar bear.

Ursa Major is the six hunters with sling shots
and the fox gnawing antlers.

Cassiopeia is the five reindeer
wading in the Milky Way (Pebbly River).

Shooting stars are the children
sledding down hills.

2.

t is time for a Night Chant,

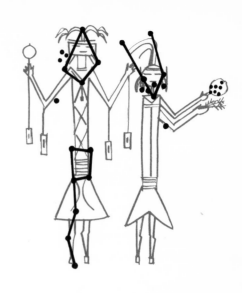

he star patterns on the rattles
nclude Auriga, Ursa Major,
e Pleiades, Hyades, and Taurus.

3.

full taught men to use manioc for food,

rion is the large frame for drying manioc. Larger stars are the tops of posts.
rius is the end of the cross beam supporting the frame from the side.
eiades is the heap of grated manioc.
debaran is the ball of pulp.

OTE: THE FOLLOWING HAVE NO CONSTELLATION PATTERNS

. The stars are silver reindeer,

4. Sibu, the god-who-builds

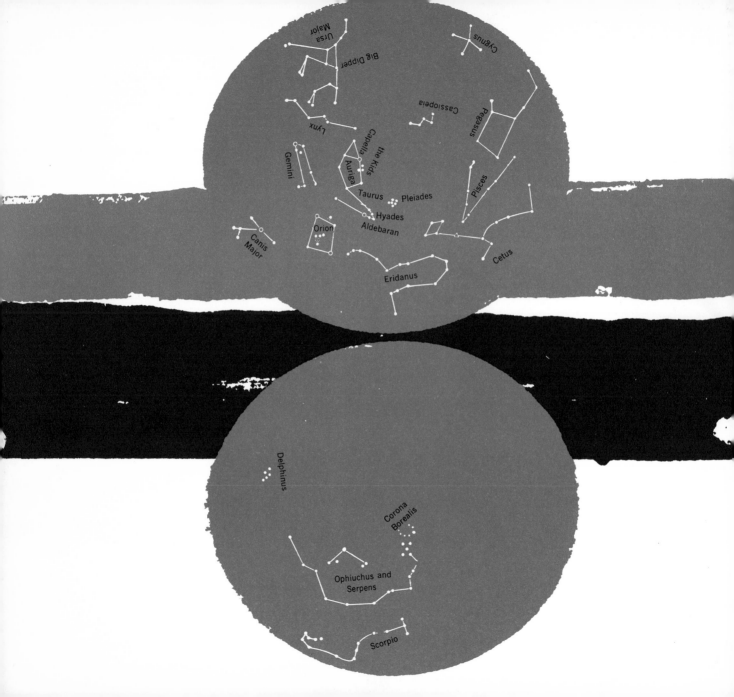